Byte Me

JIM DAVIS

RR
RAVETTE PUBLISHING

First published by Ravette Publishing 1999

Printed and bound in Great Britain
for Ravette Publishing Limited,
Unit 3, Tristar Centre,
Star Road, Partridge Green,
West Sussex RH13 8RA
by Cox & Wyman Ltd, Reading, Berkshire

ISBN: 1 84161 009 7

BYTE ME

GARFIELD, YOU ATE THE WHOLE BOX OF DOUGHNUTS

YET YOU SEEM DEPRESSED

COULD IT BE GUILT?!
THEY WERE MY FRIENDS
JIM DAVIS 12-5

COFFEE, GARFIELD?
DAILY NEWS

DAILY NEWS
JIM DAVIS 12-6
© 1996 PAWS, INC./Distributed by Universal Press Syndicate

IT'S A LITTLE STRONG
IT'S WINKING AT ME
DAILY NEWS

WHAT ARE YOU SO HAPPY ABOUT?

I WAS BEING SARCASTIC
THIS IS HAPPY
JIM DAVIS 12-7

IT'S THE HOLIDAY SEASON!
DECEMBER
JIM DAVIS 12-9

I JUST LOVE THIS TIME OF YEAR

IT MAKES ME FEEL GREEDY ALL OVER!

HMM...

I WONDER WHO FIRST CAME UP WITH THE IDEA FOR CANDY CANES?
© 1996 PAWS, INC./Distributed by Universal Press Syndicate

PROBABLY A GIMPY OLD ELF
JIM DAVIS 12-10

Merry Christmas
Love, Jon, Odie and Garfield

A-HEM
JIM DAVIS 12-11

Merry Christmas
Love, Jon, ~~Odie and Garfield~~
Garfield and Odie

JIM DAVIS 12-12

BAM BAM BAM

SMOOOOOOCH

ODIE
JIM DAVIS 12-13

ODIE

ODIE

1, 2, 3, 4, 5...
JIM DAVIS 12-14

SIX! YES!! SIX!!
GOT ANOTHER ONE!

DAILY PRESENT COUNT

LOOKS LIKE IT'S GONNA BE A GOOD CROP THIS YEAR!
JIM DAVIS 12-16

CAN'T WAIT FOR THE HARVEST

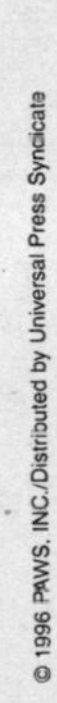

YES, THEY'RE ALMOST RIPE

THIS ONE WORKS...
THIS ONE WORKS...
THIS ONE WORKS...

ZZZZT!

I FOUND THE SHORT IN THE TREE LIGHTS!
DO TELL
JIM DAVIS 12-17

I'M LEAVING YOUR PRESENT UNDER THE TREE

I'M TRUSTING YOU NOT TO PEEK
YOU HAVE MY WORD OF HONOR
© 1996 PAWS. INC./Distributed by Universal Press Syndicate

UNCROSS YOUR TOES
YOU LITTLE FINKS
JIM DAVIS 12-18

GARFIELD, ARE YOU PEEKING AT YOUR PRESENT?
NO, I'M NOT PEEKING...

I'M TAKING A BIG FAT LOOK! TRY AND STOP ME!

HEY! THERE'S NOTHING IN HERE!
I PUT OUT A DECOY
JIM DAVIS 12-19

YOU TRICKED ME! THERE'S NOTHING IN THIS PRESENT!
YOU PROMISED ME YOU WOULDN'T PEEK

THAT'S WHAT YOU GET FOR PEEKING
© 1996 PAWS, INC./Distributed by Universal Press Syndicate

WELL THANKS FOR NOTHING!
JIM DAVIS 12-20

GARFIELD
JIM DAVIS 12-21

ODIE

PRESENT ENVY

JIM DAVIS 12-23

CANDY CANES ALWAYS TASTE BEST RIGHT AROUND CHRISTMAS
© 1996 PAWS, INC./Distributed by Universal Press Syndicate

SO EAT 'EM QUICK, WHILE THEY'RE IN SEASON!

JIM DAVIS 12-24

TAP
TAP
TAP
© 1996 PAWS, INC./Distributed by Universal Press Syndicate

CHRISTMAS EVE

GARFIELD

GARFIELD
JIM DAVIS 12-25

MERRY CHRISTMAS
GARFIELD

GARFIELD, HAVE YOU TRIED ON THE STOCKING CAP MOM MADE FOR YOU?
YES
JIM DAVIS 12-26

WHAT DO YOU THINK?

I THINK TOO MANY BALLS OF YARN GAVE THEIR LIVES FOR THIS THING

I'M WRITING A THANK-YOU CARD TO MOM AND DAD. WANT TO ADD ANYTHING?

BURPRP
© 1996 PAWS, INC./Distributed by Universal Press Syndicate

Garfield says; thank you for the Christmas Cookies
JIM DAVIS 12-27

JO-ANN, IT'S JON ARBUCKLE. I WAS WONDERING IF YOU WERE DOING ANYTHING ON NEW YEARS E-
CLICK

I DON'T BELIEVE IT...

HER **ANSWERING MACHINE** HUNG UP ON ME!
A BAD DAY IN DATEVILLE
JIM DAVIS 12-28

I'VE CALLED EVERY GIRL I KNOW, GARFIELD
JIM DAVIS 12-30

NONE OF THEM WILL GO OUT WITH ME ON NEW YEAR'S EVE
© 1996 PAWS, INC./Distributed by Universal Press Syndicate

I'M GETTING DESPERATE
I FIGURED THAT WHEN YOU DIALED THE TIME AND TEMPERATURE LADY

GARFIELD, IT'S ALMOST MIDNIGHT...

HE'S A REAL PARTY ANIMAL
© 1996 PAWS, INC./Distributed by Universal Press Syndicate
JIM DAVIS 12-31

Z

YOING
OING
OING
OING
OING

WHOO! WHAT A NIGHT!
HAPPY NEW YEAR
JIM DAVIS 1-1

STOMP
© 1997 PAWS, INC./Distributed by Universal Press Syndicate

JIM DAVIS 1-2

JIM DAVIS 1-3

PAT
PAT
PAT
JIM DAVIS 1-4

THERE'S CAT HAIR ON THE FLOOR
JIM DAVIS 1-6

AND YOU KNOW WHAT THAT MEANS, DON'T YOU?

WHOA! YOU DON'T SUPPOSE THERE'S A CAT IN THE VICINITY?!

BONK!
JIM DAVIS 1-7

THAT'S THE EIGHTH TIME YOU'VE HIT ME WITH THAT BALL TODAY!
© 1997 PAWS, INC./Distributed by Universal Press Syndicate

DON'T YOU HAVE ANYTHING TO SAY FOR YOURSELF?
WHAT'S THE RECORD?

YES, MRS. BROWN?

GARFIELD'S CLAWING AT YOUR DOOR?
© 1997 PAWS, INC./Distributed by Universal Press Syndicate

TURN OFF THE CAN OPENER, MRS. BROWN
JIM DAVIS 1-8

JON SAYS I NEVER PAY ATTENTION TO HIM
JIM DAVIS 3-8

WATCH ME PROVE HOW WRONG HE IS

YOU DID SOMETHING WITH YOUR HAIR, RIGHT, JON?

WHEN DO YOU WANT ME TO WAKE YOU?

WHEN YOU FEEL REAL BRAVE

THAT SHOULD GET ME TO THE MILLENNIUM
JIM DAVIS 1-10

YOU MUST BE ONE OF THOSE CATS I'VE HEARD SO MUCH ABOUT
JIM DAVIS 3-6

AM I SUPPOSED TO BE BARKING?

AHEM... BARK
FIRST DAY ON THE JOB

A BIG BEAR HUG, AND I'M
READY TO FACE THE DAY!

BETTER TAKE TWO...
IT'S MONDAY
JIM DAVIS 1-13

CAT!
SMACK
JIM DAVIS 3-13

UH-OH

BERNIE! ARE YOU OKAY?! WHAT CAN WE DO?!
SUBSCRIBE TO A BIGGER MAGAZINE

Z

GARFIELD!
DINNER!
Z

JIM DAVIS 1-15

YOU CAN'T DO THIS TO ME!

I DEMAND THE RIGHT TO CALL MY ATTORNEY!

NOW GET ME A TELEPHONE BOOK, BOZO!
THIS IS TOO EASY
JIM DAVIS 3-11

I'M DEPRESSED, GARFIELD

AFTER I'M GONE, NO ONE WILL CARE THAT I EVER EXISTED
HEY, CHEER UP, JON
© 1997 PAWS, INC./Distributed by Universal Press Syndicate
www.uexpress.com

THEY DON'T CARE NOW
JIM DAVIS 3-17

I'M GOING TO WORK

AND I'LL DO NOTHING!

LET'S HEAR IT FOR YIN AND YANG
JIM DAVIS 1-18

DO-NUTS

GOBBLE
MUNCH
SMACK
GULP
DO-NUTS

DO-NUTS
JIM DAVIS 3-14

I SHALL NOW TOSS THIS BIRD INTO THE AIR AND CATCH IT IN MY MOUTH!

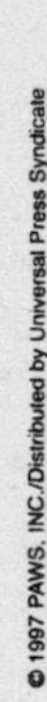

I AM SOOO STUPID
JIM DAVIS 1-21

SAD NEWS FROM HOME, GARFIELD
JIM DAVIS 3-21

"DEAR SON: YOUR PET HOG, EARL, HAS PASSED AWAY."
© 1997 PAWS, INC./Distributed by Universal Press Syndicate

"ENCLOSED ARE SOME DELICIOUS SAUSAGE PATTIES"
WELL, I'M THROUGH GRIEVING. LET'S EAT!

THIS DOGGY SWEATER FEELS PRETTY GOOD ON A COLD DAY

HA HA HA HA HA HA HA HA HA HA HA HA!

NOW IT'S A LITTLE TOO WARM
JIM DAVIS 1-23

SOON JON'S FOOD WILL BE MINE!

I ATE LUNCH EARLY TODAY
OH, GREAT!
© 1997 PAWS, INC./Distributed by Universal Press Syndicate
www.uexpress.com

NOW, WHAT AM I SUPPOSED TO DO WITH THIS SNEAK
EXPRESSION?!
JIM DAVIS 3-19

THERE'S NO NEWS TODAY

BECAUSE EVERYBODY EVERYWHERE SPENT ALL DAY WATCHING TV
© 1997 PAWS, INC./Distributed by Universal Press Syndicate
JIM DAVIS 1-25

LOOKS LIKE WE'RE GOING TO HAVE TO START TAKING TURNS

HEY, GARFIELD, GUESS WHAT? IT SNOWED LAST NI-
JIM DAVIS 1·27

SPLAP!

TELL ME SOMETHING I DON'T KNOW
THIS IS WAR!

SLUUUUCK

JIM DAVIS 2-18
© 1997 PAWS, INC./Distributed by Universal Press Syndicate

CRUNCH
CRONCH
CRUNCH
THE DIET, DAY ONE

JIM DAVIS 1-29

WOO WOO WOOOO
JUST CALL HIM "MISTER POWDER PANTS"

THIS HAS BEEN A BAD DAY, GARFIELD

AND NO WONDER

SOMEONE STUCK A "BURY ME ALIVE" SIGN ON MY BACK!
YES, SOME DAYS ARE BETTER THAN OTHERS
BURY ME ALIVE
JIM DAVIS 2-15

SNOWBALL FIGHTING IS SO BARBARIC
JIM DAVIS 1-31

FLING!

SPLOOT!
UHHH-AH-EEE-AH-EEE-AHH-EEE-AHH
THUMP THUMP
THUMP
THUMP
GAR-FIELD!

I KNOW YOU'RE SICK OF CARROT STICKS, SO I FIXED YOU SOMETHING DIFFERENT

DICED CARROTS!
© 1997 PAWS, INC./Distributed by Universal Press Syndicate

BOY! THAT'S UNCOMFORTABLE
JIM DAVIS 2·22

SIGH...

GARFIELD! ARE YOU ALL RIGHT?
YEAH...
© 1997 PAWS, INC./Distributed by Universal Press Syndicate

NOTHING A CUP OF HOT CHOCOLATE COULDN'T CURE
JIM DAVIS 2-3

YAWN
JIM DAVIS 2-20

YOU SLEPT THROUGH BREAKFAST...
WHOOP DEE-DOO

AND MISSED YOUR MORNING CARROT STICK
REMIND ME TO SLEEP THROUGH LUNCH, TOO

AREN'T YOU GOING TO EAT ME?
NO. YOU'RE A HALLUCINATION

THIS DIET IS MAKING ME NUTS! WHATEVER FOOD I THINK OF JUST-

WHOOOO'S HUNGRY?!
JIM DAVIS 2·26

READY, GARFIELD? LET'S GO!
JIM DAVIS 2-6

AEEEE!
© 1997 PAWS, INC./Distributed by Universal Press Syndicate

ENOUGH PRACTICE... LET'S GO FOR IT!
WHY AM I UP FRONT?

EAT ME!

DAY SEVEN OF THE DIET: THE HALLUCINATIONS BEGIN
JIM DAVIS 2-24

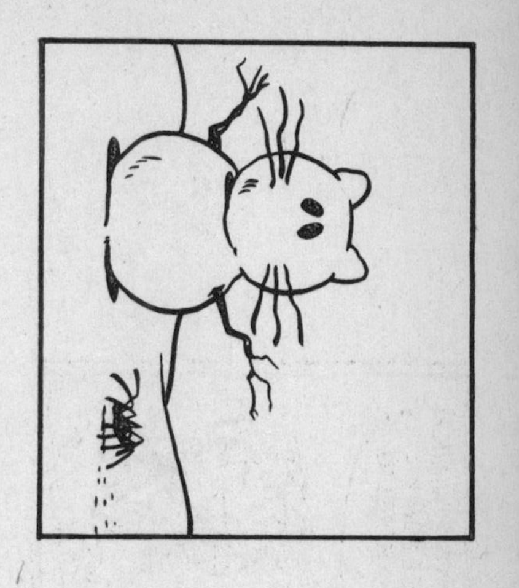

KICK
HA!

JIM DAVIS 2-8

YOU KNOW WHAT THE MAIN DIFFERENCE IS BETWEEN YOU AND ME, GARFIELD?

INTELLECT?

I DON'T SAY "MEOW"
LIKE I SAID
JIM DAVIS 3-3

I'M TAKING ODIE FOR A WALK

BY THE WAY, WE'RE OUT OF HELIUM
JIM DAVIS 2-11

HOW'S IT GOING, SCALE?
NOT SO GOOD... YOU?

AWFUL. THIS DIET IS KILLING ME
SOUNDS LIKE WE COULD BOTH USE A GOOD LAUGH...
© 1997 PAWS, INC./Distributed by Universal Press Syndicate

WHY DON'T YOU HOP ON?
JIM DAVIS 2·28

I LOVE THE CITY!

ANYTHING YOU WANT IS RIGHT HERE
© 1997 PAWS, INC./Distributed by Universal Press Syndicate
JIM DAVIS 2-13

HEY, BUDDY, WANNA BUY A BAD SUIT?
SURE!
TAXI!

I ATTRACT FUN, GARFIELD

"BE PREPARED TO PARTY", THAT'S MY MOTTO
JIM DAVIS 2-14

YUP...YOU GOTTA BE READY
HE FILLED HIS POCKETS WITH AVOCADO DIP

HERE COMES JON!
© 1997 PAWS, INC./Distributed by Universal Press Syndicate

SPLOT
FLING
JIM DAVIS 1-30

OOPS A LITTLE LOW

JIM DAVIS 2-17

MY CHAIR SEEMS TO BE SINKING INTO THE FLOOR

TIME TO DIET, GARFIELD
GIVE ME ONE GOOD REASON!

JIM DAVIS 1-28
OKAY, GARFIELD, I'M READY!

♫!
© 1997 PAWS, INC./Distributed by Universal Press Syndicate

NEVER BUILD YOUR FORT AT THE BOTTOM OF A HILL
YAAHH!

HERE'S YOUR LEAF OF LETTUCE

THANKS

AND HERE'S YOUR LOOK OF DISGUST
JIM DAVIS 2-19

Z
JIM DAVIS 2-4

BRRRIINNG

I HAVE AN IDEA. WHY DON'T YOU **NOT** DIET, AND THEN CHEAT ON THAT BY DIETING?

YOU HAVE A WEIRD HAIR GROWING OUT OF YOUR EAR
JIM DAVIS 2-21

PAT
PAT
PAT
JIM DAVIS 2-1

TINK

IT'S A
SICKNESS

THAT WAS SOME SLED RIDE, HUH, GARFIELD

PRETTY FAST, HUH, GARFIELD
JIM DAVIS 2-7

GARFIELD?
CAN WE GO BACK AND PICK UP MY LIPS?

C'MON, WHY DON'T YOU EAT ME?
BECAUSE YOU'RE A HALLUCINATION, THAT'S WHY!

BESIDES, I PREFER CHOCOLATE DOUGHNUTS

NOOO PROBLEM!
SIGH
JIM DAVIS 2-25

I HATE SNOW

WOOOOOOSSSH
© 1987 PAWS, INC./Distributed by Universal Press Syndicate
JIM DAVIS 2-5

AND THE FEELING IS MUTUAL

YOU DIET HALLUCINATIONS ARE DRIVING ME CRAZY!
JIM DAVIS 2-27

A DOUGHNUT AND A PIZZA... ALL THAT'S MISSING IS A-

HI, BIG BOY
TAP TAP
WELL, THE GANG'S ALL HERE

JIM DAVIS 2-12

TAILS

TWO OUT OF THREE?
FORGET IT. THE TV REMOTE IS MINE TONIGHT

I'M PROUD OF YOU, GARFIELD

YOU STUCK TO YOUR DIET, AND ACTUALLY LOST A FEW POUNDS
I KNOW

AND I CAN'T WAIT TO FIND THOSE SUCKERS AGAIN!
JIM DAVIS 3-1

JIM DAVIS 2·10

HERE, JON. HAVE THE COOKIE ODIE LICKED
© 1997 PAWS, INC./Distributed by Universal Press Syndicate

WHY, GARFIELD, THIS IS SO UNLIKE YOU
NO, IT'S NOT

JIM DAVIS 3-4

© 1997 PAWS, INC./Distributed by Universal Press Syndicate

NOW THAT I'VE PUT ALUMINUM SIDING ON ODIE, WE WON'T HAVE TO PAINT HIM!

WE'RE IN A RUT, GARFIELD. MAYBE I SHOULD CHANGE YOUR NAME

I'M GOING TO CALL YOU "BINGO"!

BAD BINGO!
IT'S SOUNDING BETTER ALREADY
JIM DAVIS 3-5

JIM DAVIS 1-11

HELLO THERE, HOW ARE YOU? I AM FINE. I SEE YOU ARE A CAT. I HAVE A CAT. HIS NAME
MITTENS. I LOVE MY CAT. HE
SITS ON MY
LAP AND I PET
HIM AND PET
HIM AND PET
© 1997 PAWS, INC./Distributed by Universal Press Syndicate

I HATE IT WHEN MIMES TAKE A BREAK

I DON'T WANT TO BE DISTURBED!
JIM DAVIS 3-7

JON'S WORKING ON A JIGSAW PUZZLE

THOSE TWO-PIECERS CAN BE VICIOUS

COMING UP ON YOUR RIGHT, LADIES AND GENTLEMEN, THE AMAZING "STAIRWAY OF BANANA PEELS"!

BONK
BONK
BONK
BONK
BONK
BONK
BONK
BONK
© 1997 PAWS, INC./Distributed by Universal Press Syndicate

AND NOW IF YOU WILL PICK UP YOUR TEETH, WE CAN MOVE ON TO THE REMARKABLE "CLOSET OF FALLING STUFF"!
JIM DAVIS 1-9

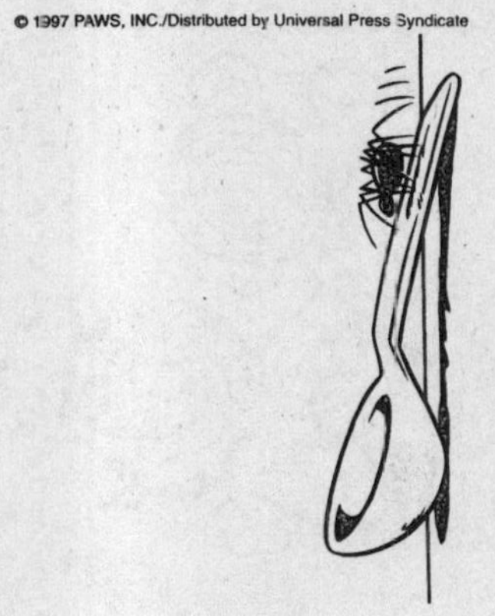

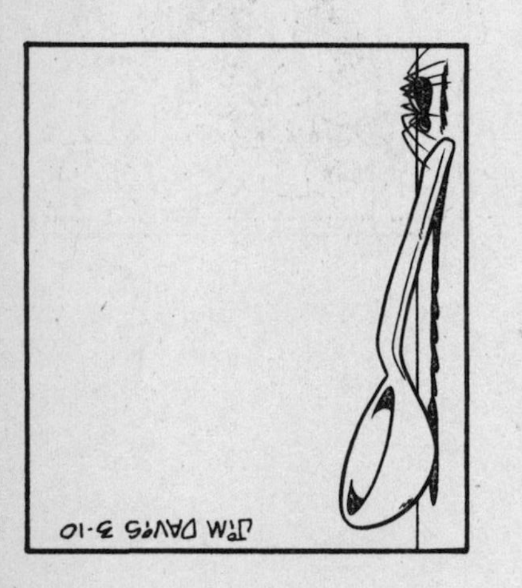
JIM DAVIS 3-10

LICK LICK
SLURP

WANT A LICK, POOKY?

JIM DAVIS 1-16

KNOW WHAT? LIFE'S JUST TOO SHORT
JIM DAVIS 3-12

SMACK

BOY, THE IRONY IS SO THICK, YOU COULD CUT IT WITH A KNIFE

UH-OH!
© 1997 PAWS, INC./Distributed by Universal Press Syndicate

JIM DAVIS 1-14

DO YOU HAVE TO STAND THAT CLOSE TO ME?
NO
© 1997 PAWS, INC./Distributed by Universal Press Syndicate

I CAN STAND THIS CLOSE
JIM DAVIS 1-20

BURP

BIG MEAL?
YOU BET

A WHOLE FLY!
WHAT A PIG
JIM DAVIS 3-15

POOKY, YOU SURE KNOW HOW TO SPOIL A GOOD BAD MOOD!
JIM DAVIS 1-17

LAP LAP LAP LAP LAP L
GAR

LAP LAP LAP LAP L
ODIE
GARFIEL
JIM DAVIS 3-18

JON! ODIE'S DRINKING OUT OF THE TOILET AGAIN!
LAP LAP LAP LAP
ODIE
GARFIELD
www.uexpress.com

I GOT YOU A GET-WELL CARD, JON
GET WELL SOON

WHAT ARE YOU DOING, GARFIELD?
WAITING FOR YOU TO FINISH THAT MONTH OLD MEAT LOAF
JIM DAVIS 1-24

PREPARE FOR A STOMPING, DAISY!
WHY DON'T YOU PICK ON SOMEONE YOUR OWN SIZE?!

A DAISY **MY** SIZE?
HEY LUTHER!
JIM DAVIS 3-20

YOU WANT A PIECE OF THIS, CAT?! ... C'MON! C'MON!
WAKE **UP**, GARFIELD... WAAAAKE **UP**
www.uexpress.com

KNOW WHAT I'M HAVING FOR DINNER, GARFIELD?

OH, I THOUGHT I'D FRY UP A LITTLE...

FISH SKELETON!
SO, WHAT ARE YOU TRYING TO SAY?
JIM DAVIS 1-22

...AND DON'T YOU FORGET IT!

YOU FORGOT IT, DIDN'T YOU?
I FORGOT IT BEFORE YOU FINISHED SAYING WHATEVER IT WAS
JIM DAVIS 3-22

HELLO, LINDA?... JON ARBUCKLE...

OK, I'LL WAIT

SHE'S PUTTING ME ON HER ANSWERING MACHINE
OUCH
JIM DAVIS 3-24

MARSHA, WILL YOU GO OUT WITH ME?
JIM DAVIS 3-25

SAY YES AND I'LL BE HAPPIER THAN A HOG WITH A MOUTH FULL OF SLOP

HELLO?...
PLATITUDE MAN STRIKES OUT AGAIN

THINK OF IT THIS WAY, JULIE
JIM DAVIS 3-26

GOING OUT WITH ME IS BETTER THAN A STICK IN THE EYE

PUT THE STICK DOWN, JULIE
NEVER GIVE'M OPTIONS, JON

I'M GOING TO IMPRESS MY DATE, GARFIELD
JIM DAVIS 3-27

SHE'LL SEE HOW NEAT AND ORGANIZED I AM

I'M TAKING MY SOCK DRAWER
THE BINKY THE CLOWN SOCKS SHOULD STAY HOME

MY DATE IS IN SHOW BUSINESS, GARFIELD

WE MET AT THE CARNIVAL
© 1997 PAWS, INC./Distributed by Universal Press Syndicate

TONIGHT I DINE WITH "ZELDA, THE TOAD WOMAN"
DON'T FORGET TO TAKE A JAR OF FLIES
JIM DAVIS 3-28

GARFIELD, I'M GONNA SLUG DOWN THIS ROOT BEER...
JIM DAVIS 3-29

THEN I'M GONNA GO TALK TO THAT CHICK

BURP!
AH, LOVE
CRETIN!

GARFIELD, HOW WOULD YOU LIKE BREAKFAST IN BED THIS MORNING?

SURE

FILL 'ER UP!
JIM DAVIS 3-31

I CAN'T STAND THE SMELL OF THIS PAINT!
DON'T WORRY, THE BUMSTEADS HAVE INVITED US OVER TO THEIR HOUSE

YOU MEAN WE'RE MOVING TO A DIFFERENT COMIC STRIP?
JUST UNTIL THE PAINT DRIES
JIM DAVIS 4-1

EVEN FOR APRIL FOOL'S DAY THIS IS RIDICULOUS!
G-RRR

BARK! BARK!
BARK! BA
JIM DAVIS 4-2

THE VOLUME NEEDS ADJUSTING
SQUEAK SQUEAK

BARK! BARK!
BARK! BARK!

THERE'S HARRY ROGERS
"MOST LIKELY TO SUCCEED"
JIM DAVIS 4·3

THAT'S PATTY HARRISON
"MOST LIKELY TO BECOME FAMOUS"

THERE'S ME
"MOST LIKELY TO DATE A KITCHEN APPLIANCE"

GARFIELD, GO OUT AND GET THE PAPER

© 1997 PAWS, INC./Distributed by Universal Press Syndicate

ALL RIGHT, ALL RIGHT! I'LL MOW THE LAWN!
JIM DAVIS 4-4

JIM DAVIS 4-5
KNOCK
KNOCK
KNOCK

© 1997 PAWS, INC./Distributed by Universal Press Syndicate

OPENING DAY OF FLEA SEASON
HONEY, WE'RE HOME!

I'VE DECIDED TO TAKE UP JOGGING

WHICH WILL GO WELL WITH MY OTHER HOBBY...

...LYING
JIM DAVIS 4-7

HEY, GARFIELD, LET'S PLAY "CATCH"

BOINK

I SAID, "CATCH"
I PREFER "RICOCHET"
JIM DAVIS 4-8

WE NEED SOME ACTION AROUND HERE!

WIGGLING YOUR EARS DOESN'T COUNT
THEN **YOU** THINK OF SOMETHING
JIM DAVIS 4-9

THIS BOOK IS ABOUT FAITHFUL PETS, GARFIELD
JIM DAVIS 4-10

PETS WHO RISKED THEIR LIVES TO PROTECT THEIR OWNERS

YOU WOULDN'T BE INTERESTED
WHAT ABOUT THE TIME I ATE THAT HOT PIZZA TO SAVE YOU FROM BURNING THE ROOF OF YOUR MOUTH?

GARFIELD, I'M HOME!

SOME PETS SCAMPER TO GREET THEIR OWNERS

BUT, NOT YOOOOU THOUGH
I BELIEVE THE KEYWORD IS "SCAMPER"
JIM DAVIS 4-11

HERE COMES JON.
I'D BETTER LOOK BUSY

RATS! I
FORGOT HOW!
JIM DAVIS 4-12

THIS MORNING I HAD A BOWL OF CEREAL WITH STRAWBERRIES

WHEN I TURNED MY BACK, A MOUSE ATE THEM

WHAT DO YOU SAY TO THAT, GARFIELD?!
WE HAVE STRAWBERRIES?
JIM DAVIS 4-14

DO YOU KNOW WHAT'S GOING TO HAPPEN WHEN I CATCH YOU?

NOT REALLY

LET'S ASK JON. MAYBE HE KNOWS
JIM DAVIS 4-15

THOSE MICE ARE TOO MUCH, GARFIELD
JIM DAVIS 4-16

EITHER THEY GO, OR I GO!

THUMP! THUMP! THUMP!
WHAT'S THAT NOISE?
THAT'S TWENTY MICE DRAGGING YOUR SUITCASE DOWN THE STAIRS

I CAME WITHIN AN EYELASH OF CATCHING THAT PESKY MOUSE TODAY

I'M BACK FROM HAWAII!

OKAY, MAYBE IT WAS SEVERAL EYELASHES
JIM DAVIS 4-17

JIM DAVIS 4-18
THE MOUSE ESCAPED

I MEAN, THE MOUSE ESCAPED

YOU'RE NOT FOOLING ANYBODY
HOW ABOUT THIS? THE MOUSE ...

DON'T COME OUT HERE, MOUSE, OR YOU'LL REGRET IT

YOU'LL REALLY, **REALLY** REGRET IT!

WHY?
BECAUSE IT'S REALLY, **REALLY** BORING OUT HERE
JIM DAVIS 4-19

YOU LOOK LIKE YOU'RE READY FOR A NICE CLIMB
FAT CHANCE!

THERE'S A BIRD'S NEST ON THE THIRD BRANCH FROM THE TOP
© 1997 PAWS, INC./Distributed by Universal Press Syndicate

JIM DAVIS 4-21
LIAR!
SUCKER

DO TREES HAVE FEELINGS? LIKE LOVE... HATE... PAIN?
JIM DAVIS 4-22

OH, PAIN, DEFINITELY
REALLY? WHEN?

RIGHT NOW. YOU'RE STANDING ON MY ROOT
SORRY

CLIMB YOU? WHAT DO YOU THINK I AM, A DOPE?!
WILL YOU SCRATCH MY BACK THEN?

SCRATCH
SCRATCH
SCRATCH
AHHH... HIGHER... HIGHER... HIGHER...

HEY!
WHAT A DOPE
JIM DAVIS 4-23

JON WILL RESCUE ME. HE WORRIES WHEN I'M NOT AROUND. WHAT A GREAT GUY
JIM DAVIS 4-24

GOOD OL' JON. HE SHOULD BE HERE ANY MINUTE NOW
© 1997 PAWS. INC./Distributed by Universal Press Syndicate

WHERE IS THAT DORK?

OTHER GARFIELD BOOKS AVAILABLE

Pocket Books @ £2.99 each	ISBN
Double Trouble	1 84161 008 9
Flying High	1 85304 043 6
A Gift For You	1 85304 190 4
The Gladiator	1 85304 941 7
Going Places	1 85304 242 0
Great Impressions	1 85304 191 2
Hangs On	1 85304 784 8
Happy Landings	1 85304 105 X
Here We Go Again	0 948456 10 8
In The Pink	0 948456 67 1
In Training	1 85304 785 6
The Irresistible	1 85304 940 9
Just Good Friends	0 948456 68 X
Le Magnifique!	1 85304 243 9
Let's Party	1 85304 906 9
On The Right Track	1 85304 907 7
On Top Of The World	1 85304 104 1
Pick Of The Bunch	1 85304 258 7
The Reluctant Romeo	1 85304 391 5
Says It With Flowers	1 85304 316 8
Shove At First Sight	1 85304 990 5
Strikes Again	0 906710 62 6
To Eat, Or Not To Eat?	1 85304 991 3
Wave Rebel	1 85304 317 6
With Love From Me To You	1 85304 392 3

Theme Books @ £3.99 each	
Guide to Behaving Badly	1 85304 892 5
Guide to Creatures Great and Small	1 85304 998 0
Guide to Healthy Living	1 85304 972 7
Guide to Insults	1 85304 895 X
Guide to Pigging Out	1 85304 893 3
Guide to Romance	1 85304 894 1
Guide to The Seasons	1 85304 999 9
Guide to Successful Living	1 85304 973 5

Classics @ £4.99 each		ISBN
Volume One		1 85304 970 0
Volume Two		1 85304 971 9
Volume Three		1 85304 996 4
Volume Four		1 85304 997 2

Miscellaneous		
Garfield Treasury	£9.99	1 85304 975 1
Garfield Address & Birthday Book Gift Set	£7.99 inc VAT	1 85304 918 2
Garfield 21st Birthday Celebration Book	£9.99	1 85304 995 6

All Garfield books are available at your local bookshop or from the address below. Just tick the titles required and send the form with your payment to:-

B.B.C.S., P.O. BOX 941, HULL, NORTH HUMBERSIDE HU1 3YQ
24 Hour Telephone Credit Card Line 01482 224626
Prices and availability are subject to change without notice.
Please enclose a cheque or postal order made payable to B.B.C.S. to the value of the cover price of the book and allow the following for postage and packing:

U.K. & B.F.P.O.:	£1.95 (weight up to 1kg)	3-day delivery
	£2.95 (weight up to 1kg up to 20kg)	3-day delivery
	£4.95 (weight up to 20kg)	next day delivery

EU & Eire:	Surface Mail	£2.50 for first book & £1.50 for subsequent books
	Airmail	£4.00 for first book & £2.50 for subsequent books
USA:	Surface Mail	£4.50 for first book & £2.50 for subsequent books
	Airmail	£7.50 for first book & £3.50 for subsequent books
Rest of	Surface Mail	£6.00 for first book & £3.50 for subsequent books
The World:	Airmail	£10.00 for first book & £4.50 for subsequent books

Name ....

Address ....

....

....

Cards accepted: Visa, Mastercard, Switch, Delta, American Express

Expiry Date ....Signature ....